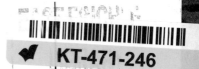

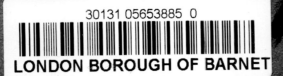

PENGUIN BOOKS

UK | USA | Canada | Ireland | Australia
India | New Zealand | South Africa

Penguin Books is part of the Penguin Random House group of companies
whose addresses can be found at global.penguinrandomhouse.com.

www.penguin.co.uk
www.puffin.co.uk
www.ladybird.co.uk

Penguin Random House UK

First published in the USA by Random House Children's Books,
a division of Penguin Random House LLC,
and in Great Britain by Penguin Books 2018

001

Images on pages 12 (bottom left), 22, 28–29,
58 (bottom left), 69, and 78 (bottom left)
are used under license from Shutterstock.com.

Printed in Italy

A CIP catalogue record for this book is available from the British Library

ISBN: 978-0-241-38838-9

All correspondence to:
Penguin Books, Penguin Random House Children's
80 Strand, London WC2R 0RL

HOW TO SURVIVE IN A STRANGER THINGS WORLD

Compiled by Matthew J. Gilbert

PENGUIN BOOKS

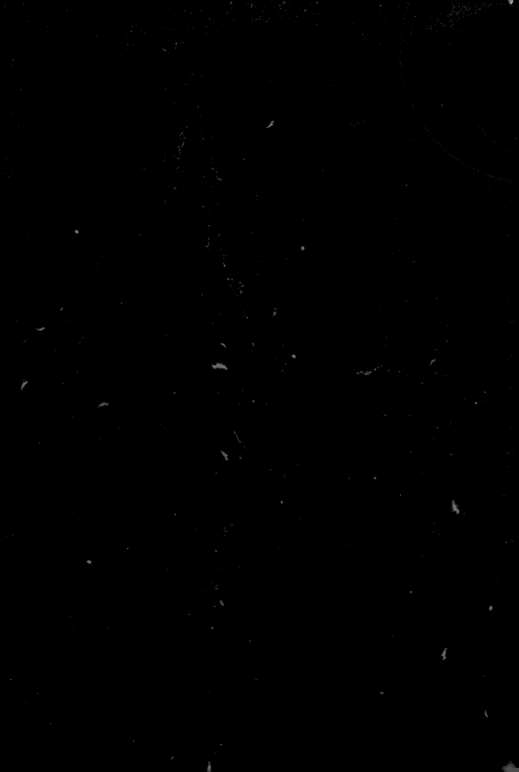

NO PLACE LIKE HOME

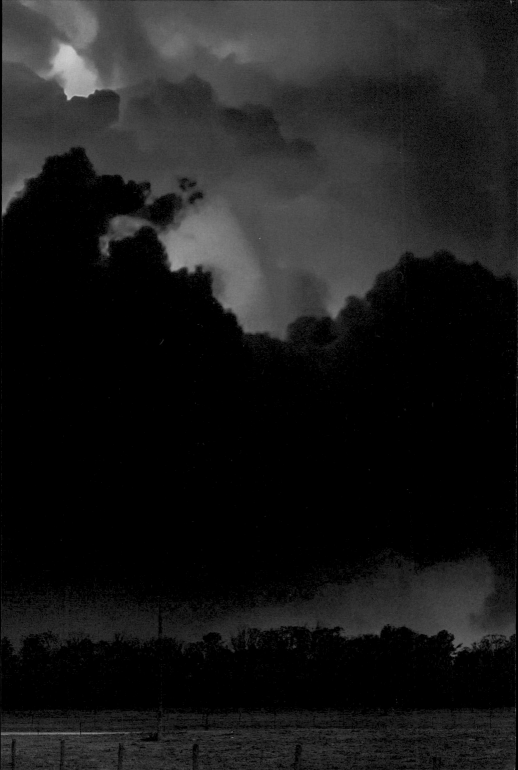

WELCOME
TO
HAWKINS

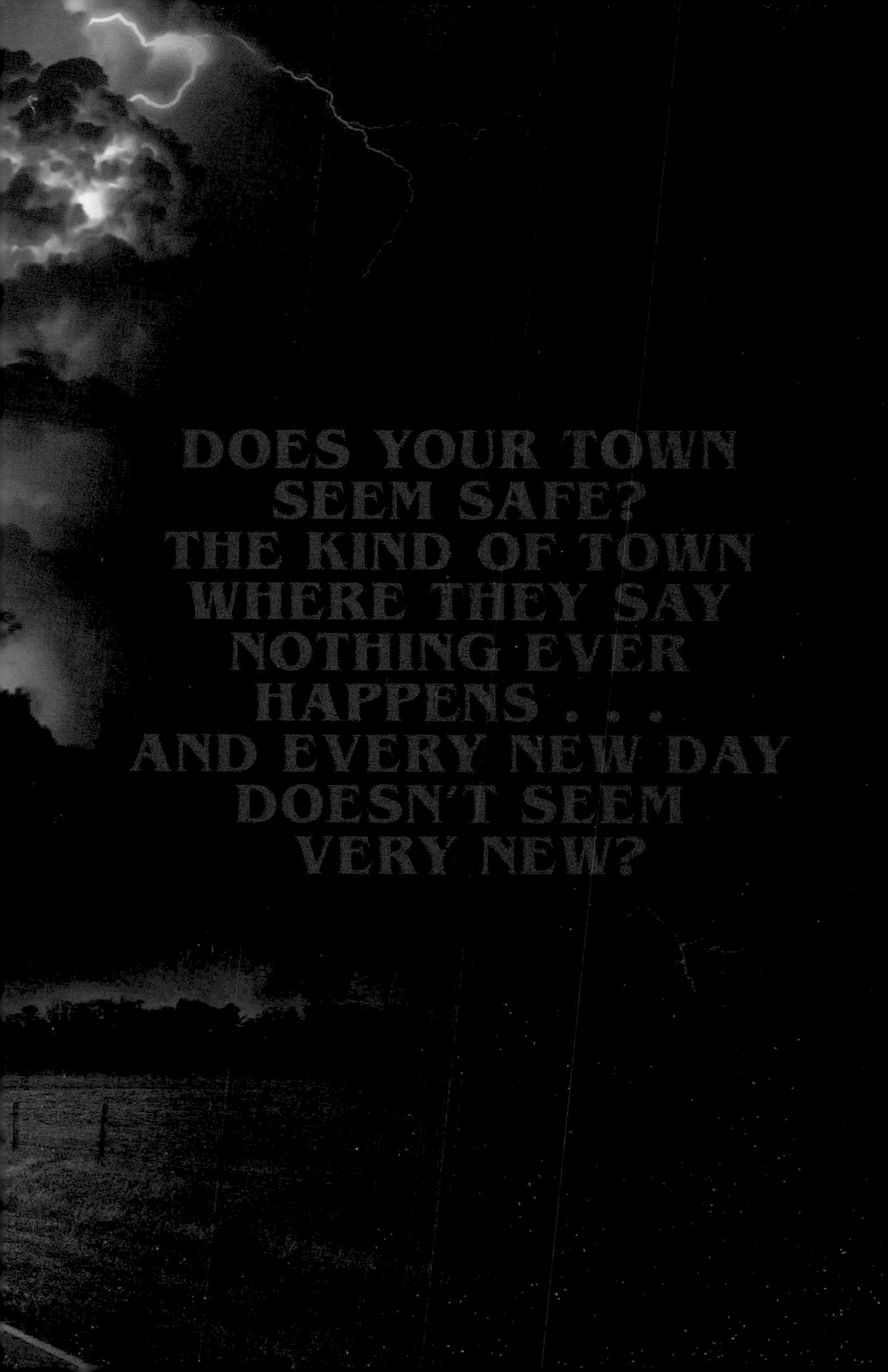

DOES YOUR TOWN
SEEM SAFE?
THE KIND OF TOWN
WHERE THEY SAY
NOTHING EVER
HAPPENS . . .
AND EVERY NEW DAY
DOESN'T SEEM
VERY NEW?

HAWKINS
POLICE
HOPPER

Mornings are for

COFFEE

&

CONTEMPLATION.

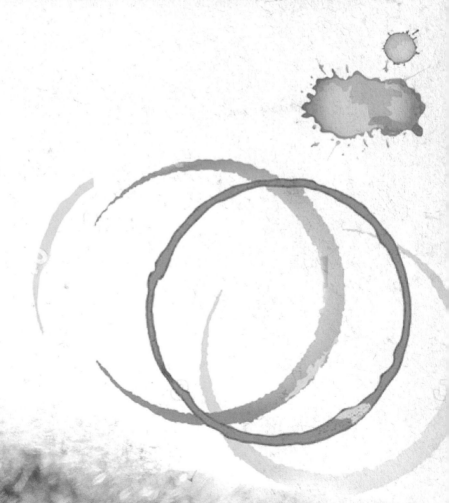

WAFFLES
ARE GOOD
anytime.

SCHOOL CAN MAKE YOU

FEEL LIKE A STRANGER.

If you want to fit in, you need to look cool—especially your hair.

Use the shampoo
and conditioner.

And when your hair's damp,
not wet, okay?

When it's damp,
you do four puffs of the
Farrah Fawcett spray.

Always be READY for a CURIOSITY voyage.

And hold on to your CURIOSITY PADDLES.

SOME
CURIOSITY
DOORS
SHOULD
STAY
LOCKED.

And when in doubt,

roll the dice.

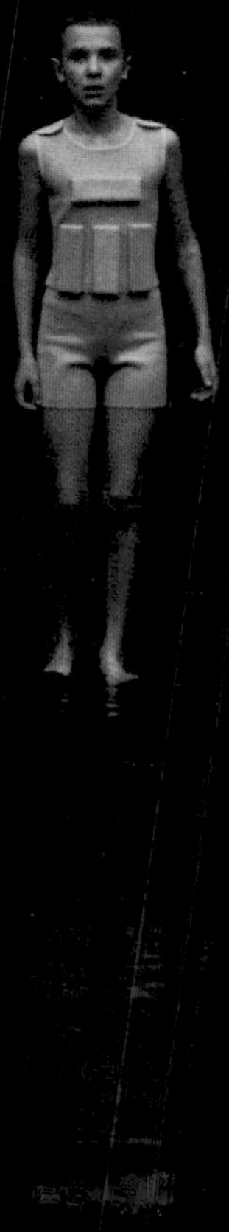

You might get
an **eleven**.

Dare to be
BITCHIN'

FRIENDS DON'T LIE

Friends
find adventure
everywhere.

Whether
it's in a
basement . . .

. . . OR ON THE DARKEST EDGES OF TOWN.

A FRIEND has your back

when things get ROCKY.

"OUR FRIEND HAS
SUPERPOWERS,
AND
SHE SQUEEZED
YOUR TINY BLADDER
WITH HER MIND!"

Did you know a stranger is just a friend you haven't met?

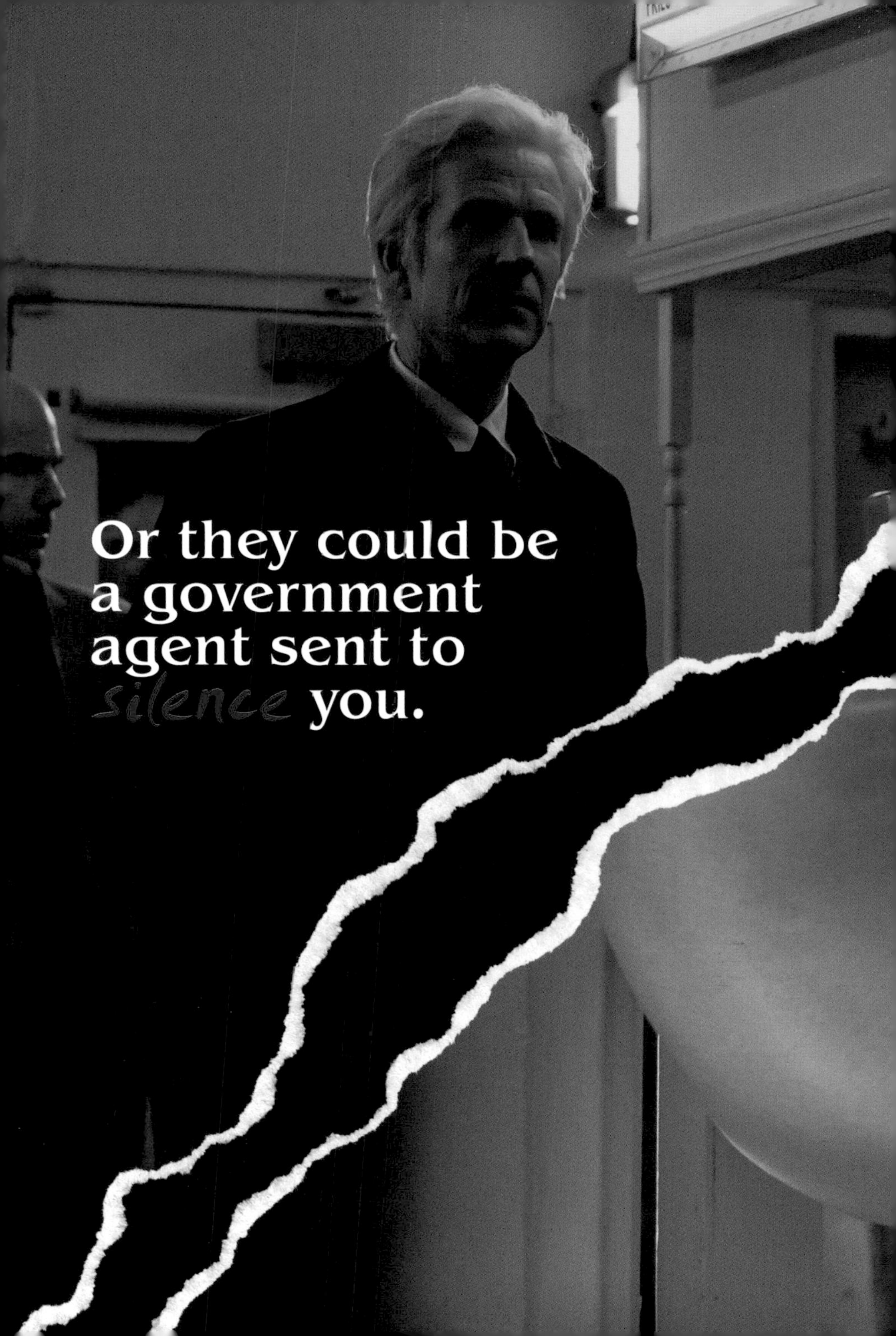
Or they could be
a government
agent sent to
silence you.

Someone who cares ALWAYS gets you.

They JUST do.

"If we're both
going crazy,

then we'll go crazy
together, right?"

Remember, your buddy is just a WALKIE-TALKIE away.

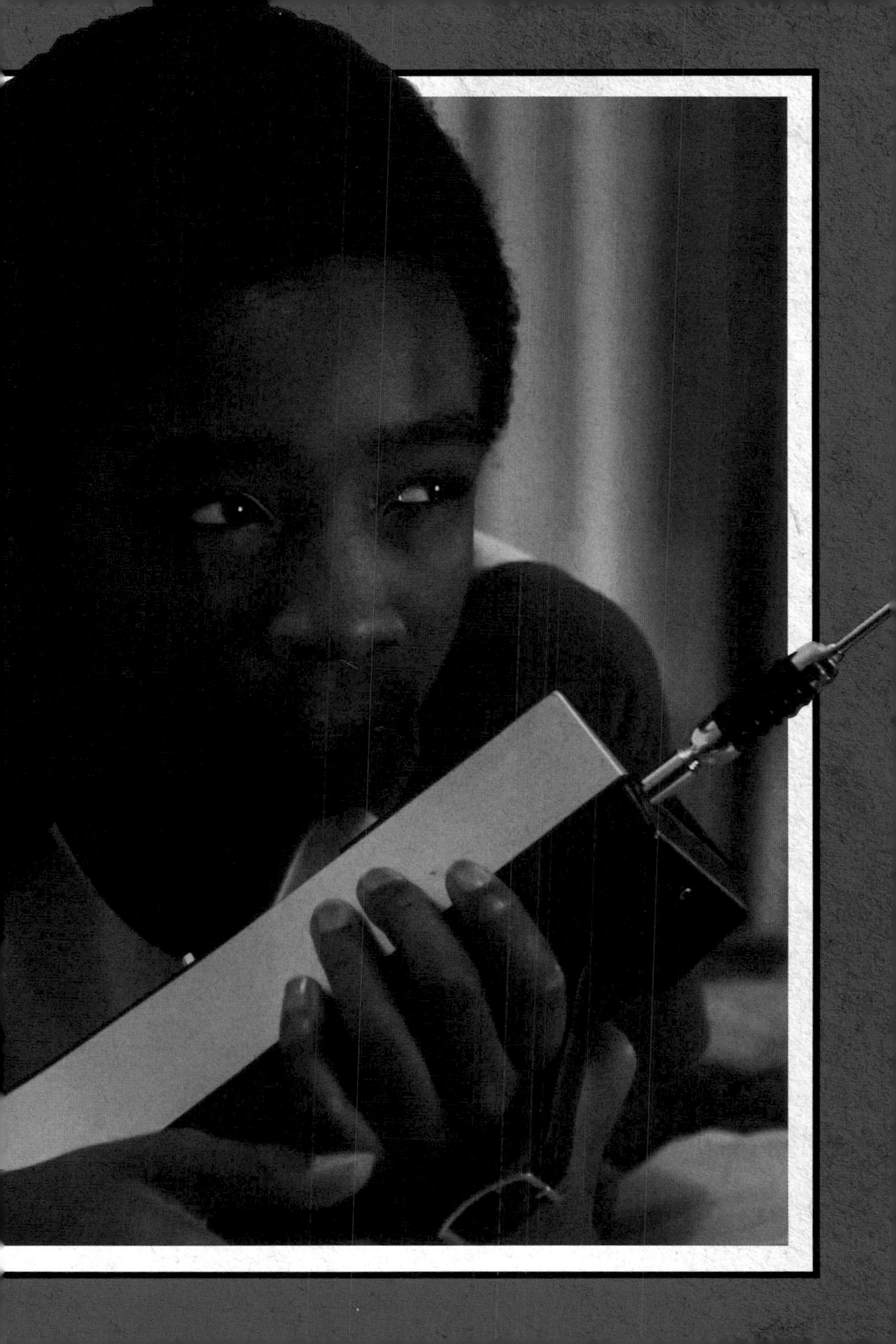

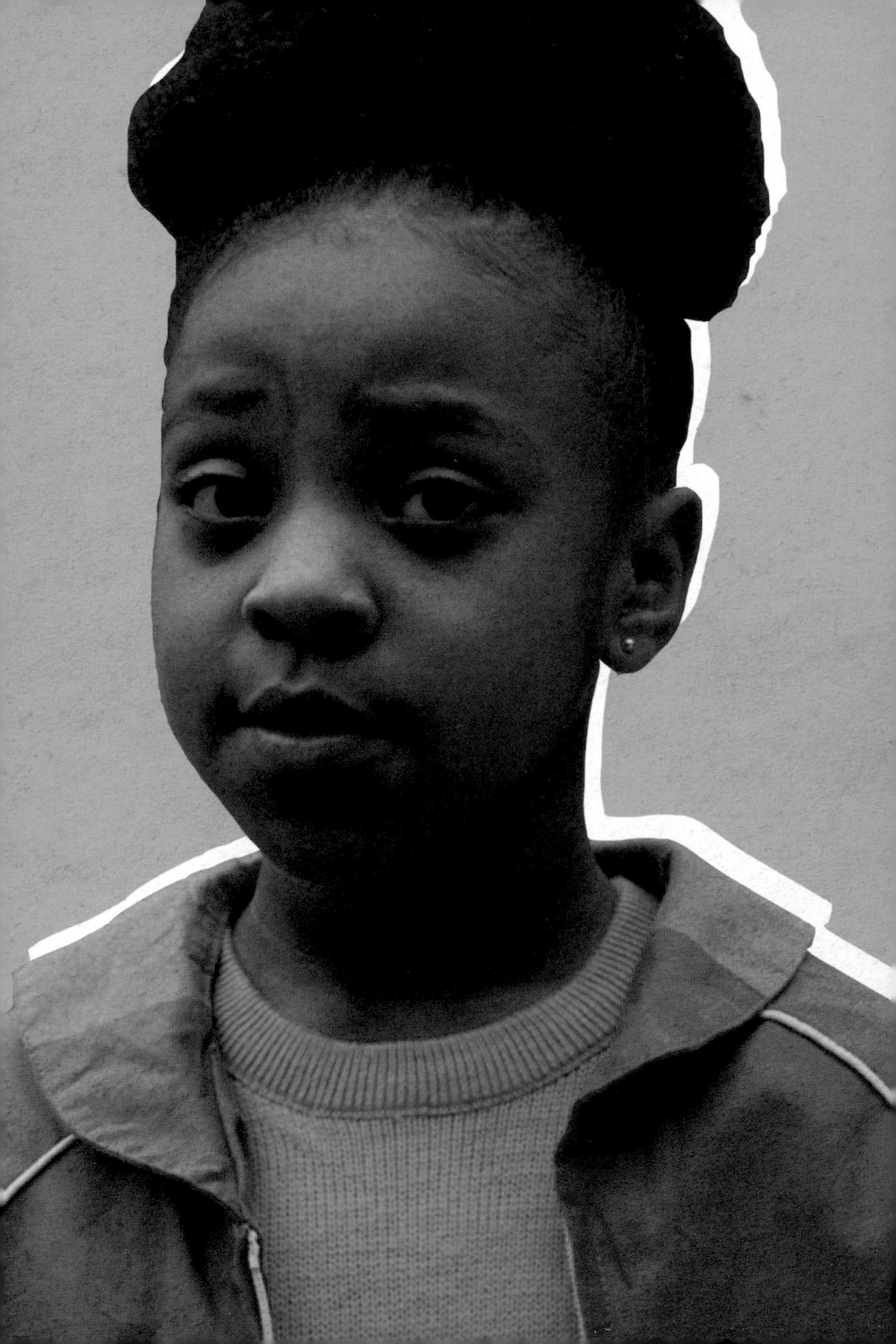

But be careful
not to say
too much.

It's called code

**SHUT
YOUR
MOUTH.**

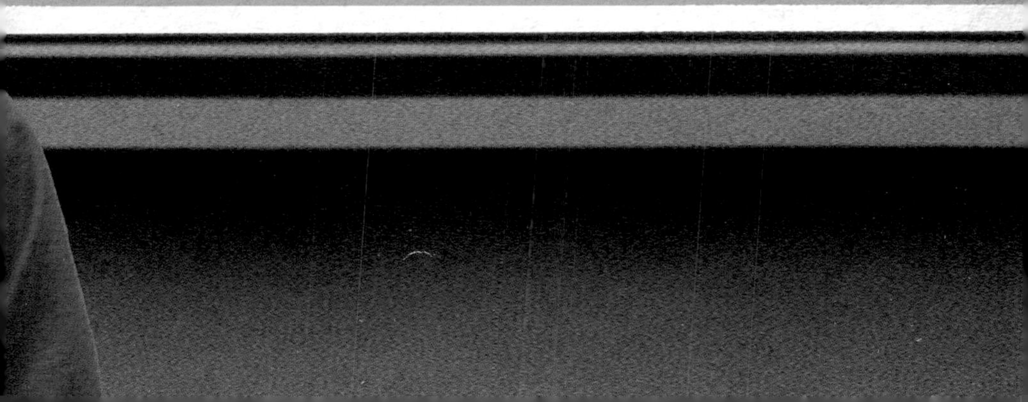

Sadly, some friends grow apart.

HAWKINS HIGH SCHOOL
GO TIGERS!
Some friends
VANISH
FOREVER.

THE UPSIDE DOWN

Sometimes you see something STRANGE

and discover your town has SECRETS.

You feel like
your world has
turned
UPSIDE DOWN.

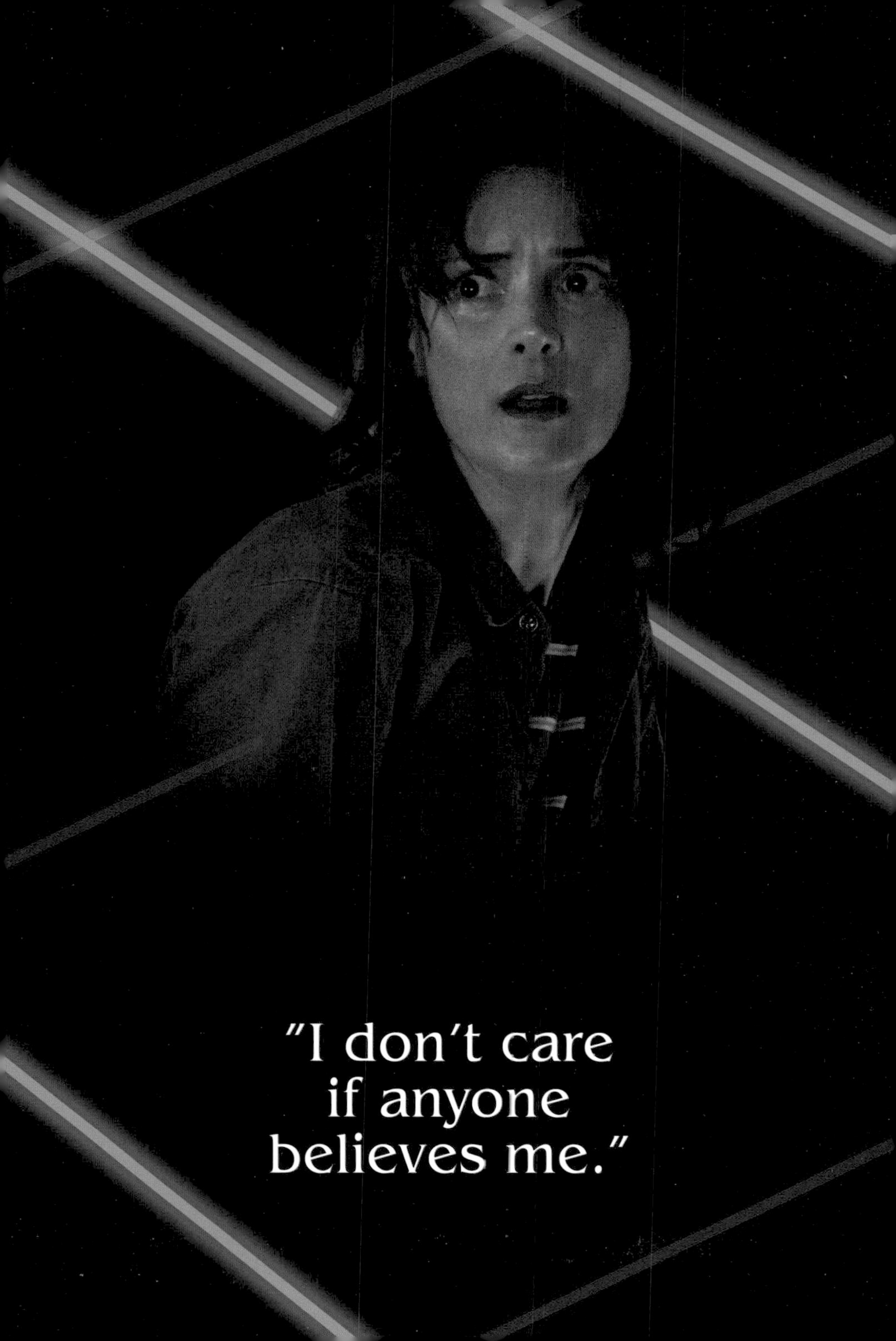
"I don't care
if anyone
believes me."

AT TIMES LIKE THIS,
IF YOU THINK
THERE'S SOMETHING
LURKING IN
THE DARK,
YOU'RE PROBABLY
RIGHT.

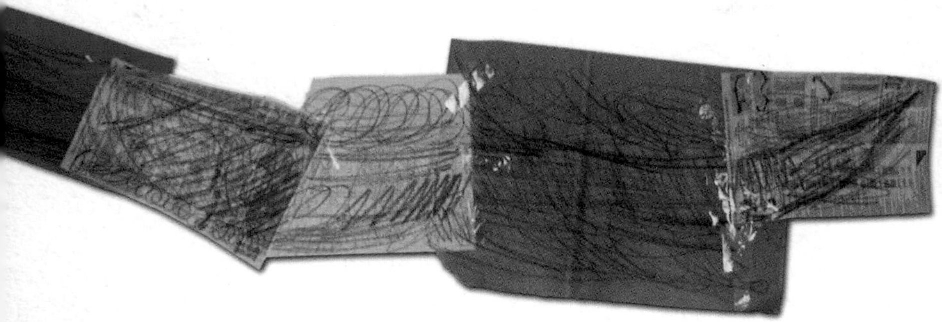

Don't be scared of
SHADOWS . . .

unless they're
SHADOW MONSTERS.

It's time to get stealthy, like a ninja.

(And carrying a baseball bat studded with nails isn't a bad idea, either.)

Don't worry.
Just stand your ground.
It will all be . . .

EASY-PEASY,
RIGHT?

You can ask your
doctor to help.

But you'd better get
a second opinion.

Don't be stupid.
Follow the rules.

RULE 1

Always keep the curtains drawn.

RULE 2

Only open the door if you hear my secret knock.

RULE 3

Never ever go outside alone especially not in daylight.

“SCIENCE IS NEAT,

but I'm afraid it's not very forgiving."

And when
you're certain
things can't get any
DARKER . . .

that's
your cue to
**LIGHT
IT
UP.**

HAWKINS

Be unstoppable.

FACE YOUR DEMONS.
LITERALLY.
THEN CRUSH THEM.

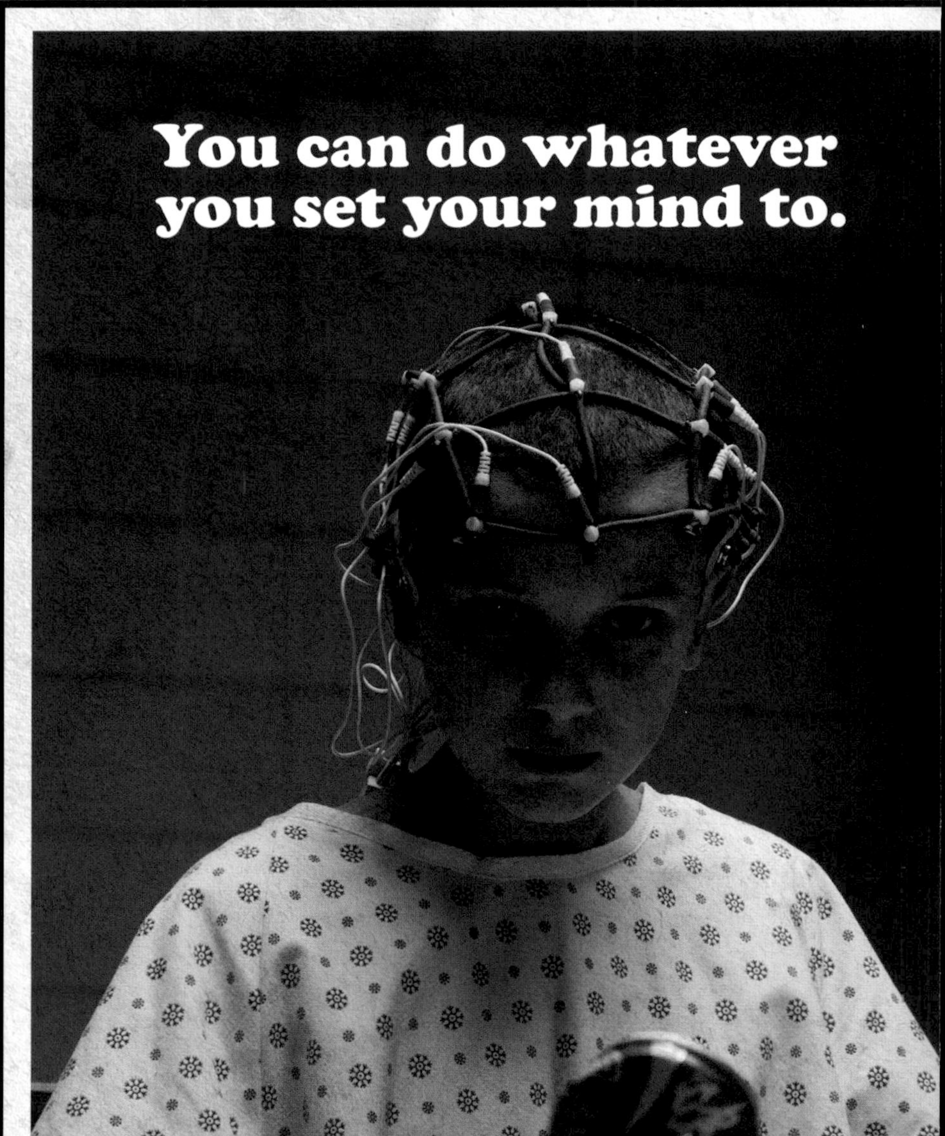
You can do whatever you set your mind to.

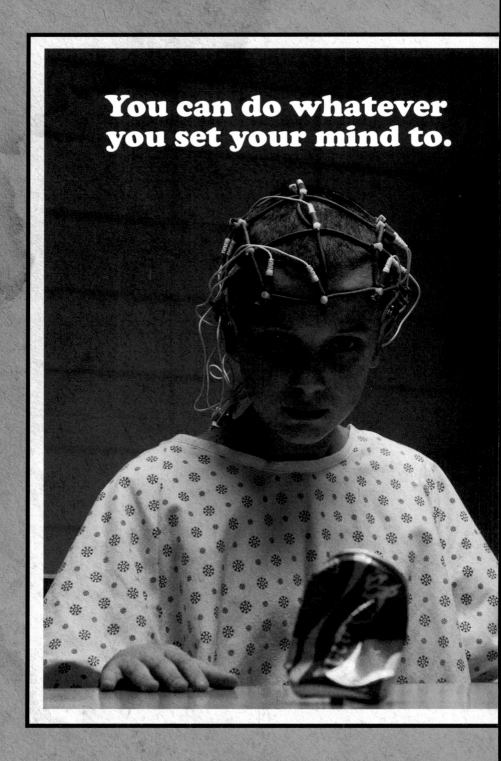

Nobody
NORMAL
ever accomplished anything meaningful in this world.

GATES ARE MEANT TO BE CRASHED. THE BIGGER AND CREEPIER, THE BETTER.

"Just be careful, all right? I can't lose you again."

"You won't lose me."

HAPPY RETURNS

When it feels like the end is near, keep your friends close . . .

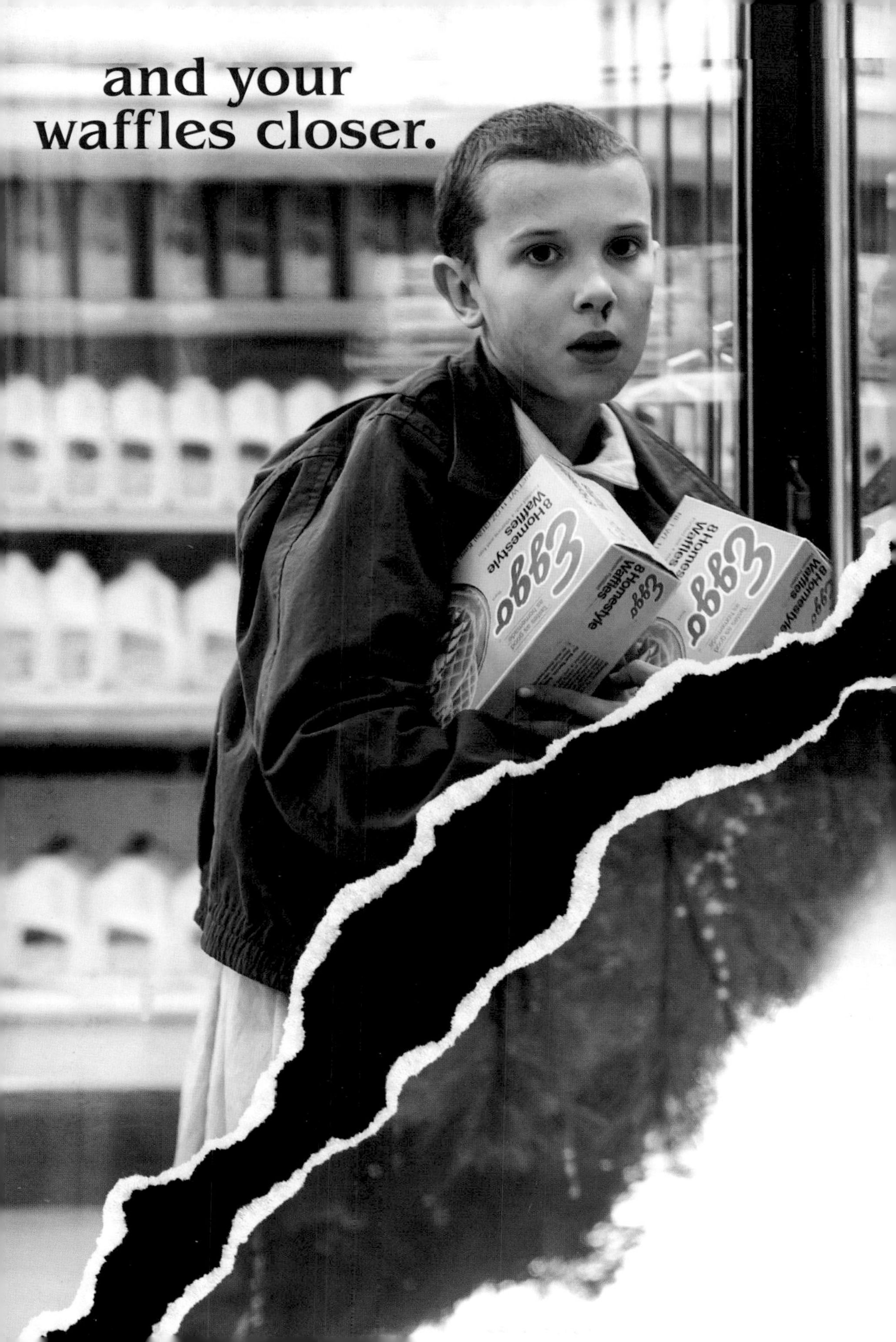
and your
waffles closer.

Snow
Ball
'84

After you've
saved the world,
you deserve a party.

Though they may dance around it, sometimes friends are meant to be more than friends.

"Do you want to dance?"
"I don't know how."

"I don't either. Do you want to figure it out?"

Nothing is gonna go
back to the way it was.
Not really.

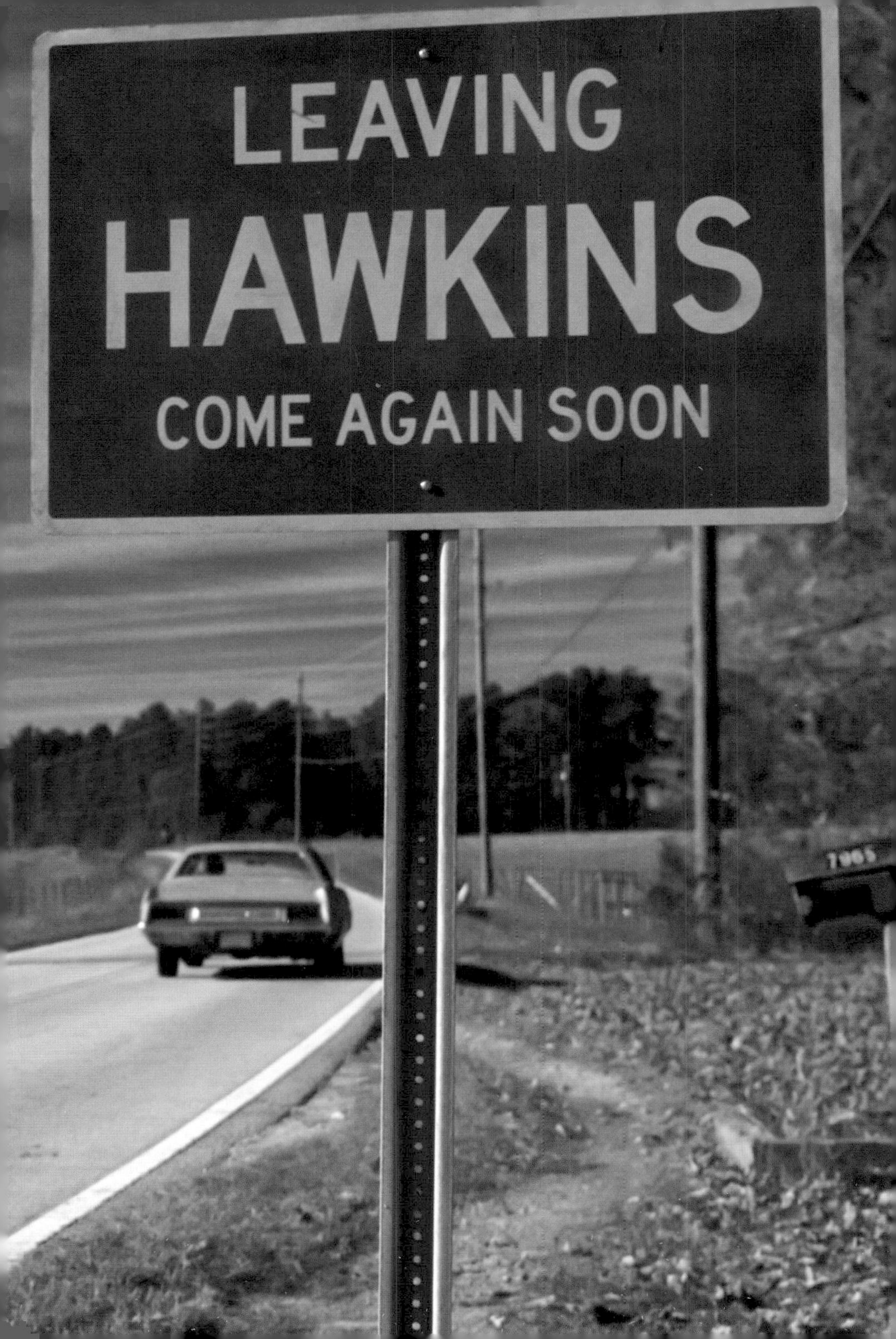
LEAVING
HAWKINS
COME AGAIN SOON

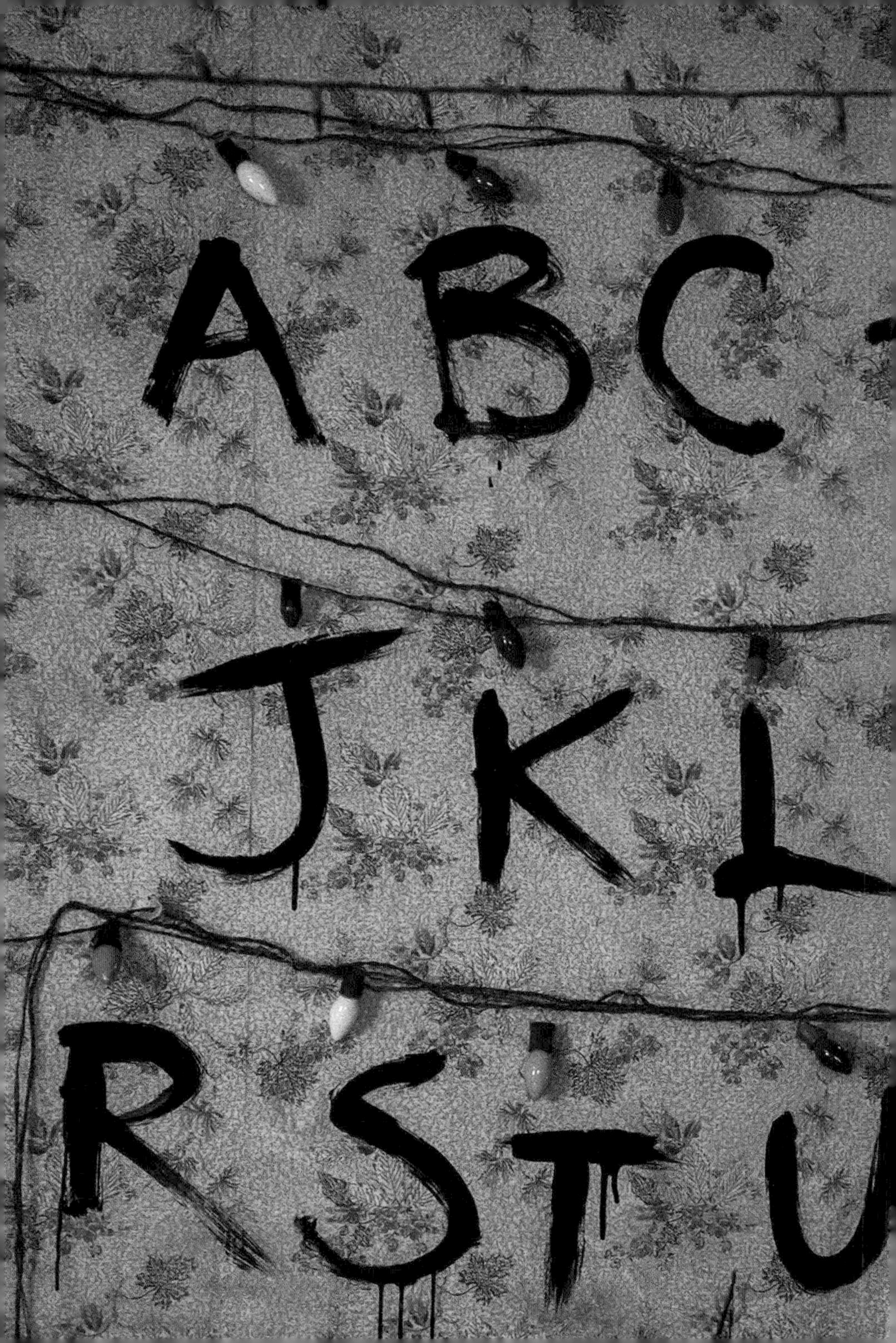
A B C
J K L
R S T U

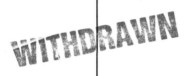

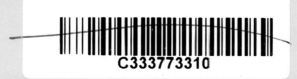